This

Bible Story Time

book belongs to

_____

_____

_____

For Lucy - E.C.

Text by Sophie Piper
Illustrations copyright © 2005 Estelle Corke
This edition copyright © 2005 Lion Hudson

The moral rights of the author and illustrator
have been asserted

A Lion Children's Book
an imprint of
Lion Hudson plc
Wilkinson House, Jordan Hill Road Road,
Oxford OX2 8DR, England
www.lionhudson.com
UK ISBN 978 0 7459 4863 8
US ISBN 978 0 8254 7814 7

First edition 2005
3 5 7 9 10 8 6 4 2

A catalogue record for this book is available
from the British Library

Typeset in 20/24 Baskerville MT Schlbk
Printed and bound in China
Distributed by:

UK: Marston Book Services Ltd, PO Box 269, Abingdon, Oxon OX14 4YN
USA: Trafalgar Square Publishing, 814 N Franklin Street, Chicago, IL 60610
USA Christian Market: Kregel Publications, PO Box 2607, Grand Rapids, Michigan 49501

BIBLE STORY TIME

Moses and the Princess

Sophie Piper ✳ Estelle Corke

LION
CHILDREN'S

Miriam smiled at her new baby brother.

'He's very special, isn't he, Mummy?' she said.

'Very special,' said her mother.

'We must both take very good care of him.'

There was a problem. Miriam and her family were Israelites. Long ago, the Israelites had been invited to live in Egypt. Now there were lots of them and the Egyptians were afraid of them.

They made them work as slaves.

The king had made a law that all Israelite baby boys must be thrown into the river. His soldiers often came looking.

Miriam's mother made a basket from reeds. She covered it with waterproof tar. She put the baby in the basket and went down to the river.

She hid her baby in his little basket among the reeds.

Miriam hid close by to watch what would happen.

The daughter of the king of Egypt came down to the river to bathe. Her servants stood on the bank.

Suddenly, the princess saw the basket.

'Please fetch that for me,' she said. 'I want to know what's inside.'

When the princess lifted the lid,
she saw the baby boy.

 'Poor little thing! He's crying!'
she said. 'He's an Israelite baby.
Someone wants to keep him safe.
I'd like to keep him.'

Miriam stepped forward. She spoke up bravely: 'If you like, I can find an Israelite woman to take care of him for you.'

'Yes please,' replied the princess.

Miriam ran home.

'Mummy!' she cried. 'Come quickly. The princess found our baby. She wants to keep him. She needs someone to look after him.'

The two hurried back as fast as they could.

The princess gave the mother her own baby.

'Please look after him for me,' she said. 'I will pay you. When the boy is old enough, he will come and live at the palace.'

'His name –' began the mother.

'Oh, yes: what shall I call him?' said the princess. 'I know: Moses.'

Moses grew up to be a prince. He lived among the Egyptians.

He was rich and powerful.

But he knew he was really an Israelite.

He was very angry at the way his people were treated. That got him into trouble, and he had to run away.

In the faraway desert, Moses became a shepherd. One day he saw a strange sight: a bush was on fire, but none of it was really burning.

The fire was a sign that God was there. God spoke to Moses.

'I want you to rescue my people. Tell the king of Egypt to let them go free.'

Moses went and asked his brother Aaron to help him. Together they went to see the king of Egypt.

'If you don't let our people go, God will send all sorts of trouble,' they pleaded.

'No,' said the king. 'No, no, no and no.'

23

There was one disaster after another: frogs hopping everywhere, flies buzzing everywhere, locusts chewing everywhere. The king would not change his mind.

The troubles got worse. The king changed his mind. Moses led his people out of Egypt, away from the cruel king.

Suddenly, the king changed his mind again. 'Hurry!' he told his army. 'Drive your chariots as fast as you can. Go and get them back.'

The people saw the army behind them.

They saw a sea in front of them.
Moses lifted his stick, and God
made a path for them through the
sea.

Safe on the other side, Miriam
danced and played the tambourine.
'God has saved us,' she sang, and
everyone joined in.